A book of birthdays and days in between for the

Child of God

◆

Mother

Father

Sisters and Brothers

Gertrud Mueller Nelson

**Illustrations by
Annika Maria Nelson**

*For Annika Maria, Sara Kirsten,
Peter Ansgar and Isabelle,
and Therese Mueller.*

*With thanks to Hildegard Mueller
Kerney, Brian Hooper, Christopher
Witt, Theresa Kubasak Turner and
Maureen Como.*

The quote on page 3 is from *Catholic
Household Blessings and Prayers.*

Gabe Huck was the editor of this book, and
Deborah Bogaert was the production editor.
The book was designed by M. Urgo and
typeset in Futura and Usherwood by Karen
Mitchell, the production artist. Electronic
colorization on the cover and back cover is
by M. Urgo. Printed by Quebecor Printing
of Kingsport, Tennessee.

Excerpts from the *Rite of Baptism for Children,*
© 1969, the *Order of Christian Funerals,*
© 1989, 1985, and the English translation of
the psalms and canticles of the *Liturgical
Psalter,* © 1994, the International Committee
on English in the Liturgy, Inc. (ICEL). Used
with permission. All rights reserved.

All other scripture quotations herein are
from the *New Revised Standard Version of the
Bible,* copyright © 1989 by the Division of
Christian Education of the National Council
of the Churches of Christ in the United States
of America. All rights reserved.

Excerpts from *Catholic Household Blessings
and Prayers* and additional blessings from
the *Book of Blessings* for use in the United
States of America © 1988 United States
Catholic Conference, Washington, D.C. Used
with permission. All rights reserved.

LITURGY
TRAINING
PUBLICATIONS

To the Parents

Good news: There's a baby on the way! Here is a book to help mark this moment, a book that will follow your child along the way. Whether you are pregnant or planning to adopt a child, these months of waiting and preparation are a time for parents to think about their child. A child takes shape as you think about her and is enriched by the imagination you expend on him. So record your dreams and write down your hopes, express your fears and foster your imagination. This is not just a baby book but a book that grows as your child grows and expands as you expand as parents.

Let this book spark your creativity and inspire your family to record and collect things. Find a place in this book for everything from a birth announcement to the child's special drawings. Tuck in school reports. Paste in envelopes containing a lock of hair or postage stamps. Put away the first written word or the first lost tooth. Collect the cards or letters written specifically to or about your child.

This book encourages you to celebrate as a family. Every family needs solid, satisfying rituals. These come with the rhythms of the day, the week, the seasons. Memories grow around our rituals.

Most pages in this book open with a short sentence or two from scripture or traditional prayers. You may wish to memorize a few of these and eventually teach them to your child.

The pages of this book will encourage you to write to your child. No need to fear the pen and blank paper: Jump in! Put down a few words and see how more come. When we write about these early years, we give words to occasions and form to what passes so quickly.

When youngsters are small, it seems hard to believe that they will ever grow up, but what oldsters say is true: "Time flies!" And it will indeed "only seem like yesterday," and this child of yours will

1

be grown and gone. The memories, the stories, the occasions you thought would be with you forever, fade easily. So write freely and simply whenever you can. Be authentic. Write what you're feeling. Write about what you observe in this child, the little things only you see: the sensitivities and character traits, the gifts and talents. Write about the happy things and the sad things that every life contains. This isn't a book about "cuteness" or perfection. Nor do you have to be a poet or your child a genius. Be genuine, and nothing you write will be unworthy.

One parent or two, adopting or giving birth, a newborn or slightly older child, the first child or the fifth — your creativity will adapt these pages to your own reality. Little by little this book will take shape, and its content will become a treasure. And over all our fumbling endeavors is the grace, love and unsearchable wisdom of God, who allows us to partake in the mystery of this child.

This is not a book to start at the beginning and conclude on the last page. Some pages relate to specific times. Get to know the book so that you can be at ease with it. Use what is helpful to you, and don't worry about the rest.

One day, when this book feels full to bursting, you will know it is time to put it away for 15 or 20 years to ripen. When your child, then grown, approaches passage into a new time, present this book as your gift. The pages will have grown poignant and moving, amusing and enlightening. No detail will seem insignificant or silly. And you will be happy for the energy you brought to this child and for the growth of character this book records and illustrates.

Then unpack its stories and memories, and send this child of yours forth with your blessing.

*May God, in whose presence
our ancestors walked, bless you.*

*May God, who has been your shepherd
from birth until now, keep you.*

*May God, who saves you from all harm,
give you peace.*

Amen.

The trees of the field shall yield their fruit, and the earth shall yield its increase.

With the help of the child's grandparents and great-grandparents,
collect the information that makes the family tree. Begin with all the family names.

_____
Parent

_____   _____
Grandparent   Grandparent

_____   _____   _____   _____
Great-grandparent   Great-grandparent   Great-grandparent   Great-grandparent

_____   _____   _____   _____
Great-great-   Great-great-   Great-great-   Great-great-
grandparent   grandparent   grandparent   grandparent

_____   _____   _____   _____
Great-great-   Great-great-   Great-great-   Great-great-
grandparent   grandparent   grandparent   grandparent

They shall be secure on their soil, and they shall know that I am the Lord.

Ezekiel 34:27

Gather what you can from the oldest family members first.
In time, collect and add more names, places, dates, occupations and stories.

_____

Parent

_____   _____

Grandparent   Grandparent

_____   _____   _____   _____

Great-grandparent   Great-grandparent   Great-grandparent   Great-grandparent

_____   _____   _____   _____

Great-great-
Grandparent   Great-great-
Grandparent   Great-great-
grandparent   Great-great-
grandparent

_____   _____   _____   _____

Great-great-
Grandparent   Great-great-
Grandparent   Great-great-
grandparent   Great-great-
grandparent

Before You Were Born

You created every part of me,
knitting me in my mother's womb.
For such handiwork, I praise you.
Awesome this great wonder!
You watched every bone
taking shape in secret,
forming in the hidden depths.
You saw my body grow
according to your design. Psalm 139

Wedding photo of parents/Family photos

Photo of mother pregnant/Sonogram photo

As We Wait for You

When Elizabeth heard Mary's greeting, the child leaped in her womb. And Elizabeth was filled with the Holy Spirit and exclaimed with a loud cry, "Blessed are you among women, and blessed is the fruit of your womb." Luke 1:41–42

Write on these four pages your hopes, fears, prayers. Record the pregnancy or tell the story of the adoption process. Write of health, home and family. Describe how everyone is preparing for this child. Describe the world this child will enter.

Adopting parents have their own variety of anticipation and preparation. The period of waiting and preparing has many of the characteristics of pregnancy. Waiting, one way or another, is a helpful prelude to acceptance and healthy bonding. Keep here cards received, announcements and something about the child's ethnic heritage.

Tell the story of the whole process from beginning to end. No detail is unimportant.

11

The Day of Your Birth

You, God, took me from the womb,
you kept me safe at my mother's breast.
I belonged to you from the time of birth,
you are my God from my mother's womb. Psalm 22

Name: _____

Date of birth and time: _____

Weight: _____ Length: _____

Place of birth (city, location, room): _____

Physician, Midwife or Social Service: _____

Others present: _____

First photo/Footprint or handprint

In those last days of waiting, what was going on? What were your feelings and thoughts? What was the weather like, and what was going on in the world? How was this child born? Remember the details: packing a bag, that last meal, timing the contractions, the labor and the delivery, the supportive, cheering community. Parents who adopt have stories to tell with many of the same small details about the arrival of this child.

Your First Days

I have relied on you since birth,
my strength from my mother's womb;
I will praise you always. Psalm 71

Front page of the newspaper from the day this child was born

Tell about that quiet, first time together, checking each other out, getting to know each other. Tell about the trip home, the waiting family, the visitors, the baby's little bed.

Tell about nursing and diapering, and the joys and difficulties of those early adjustments. Tell it all with every frustrating and wonderful detail. This is the child's creation story!

Your Name

The Lord called me before I was born,
while I was in my mother's womb the Lord named me. Isaiah 49:1

Write here about the child's names — all of them. Was the child named after someone? Why? Do these names have meanings? From what language or heritage were the names chosen? Over time, come back to this page and write down all those names of affection, nicknames, silly names and names the child makes up.

17

Your Godparents

**Holy church of God,
stretch out your hand
and welcome your children,
newborn of water
and of the Spirit of God.**

Liturgy of Baptism

Consider writing a letter to the people you have chosen
to be the godparents. Say a little in this letter about
the importance of baptism and the role of the
godparents. Tell them why they are being
asked to stand by this child. In time, invite
letters from the godparents to mark the
major events in this child's life. Keep their letters
here. Help this child form a good relationship with
the godparents.

Godparents, are you ready to help these parents in their duty as Christian mothers and fathers? Liturgy of Baptism

Your Baptism

By water and the Holy Spirit you are made a new creation.

Liturgy of Baptism

_____

Date

_____

Church and place

_____

Godparents

_____

Presider

_____

Those present

_____

_____

_____

Photos of the day/Photo of godparents

Write about preparing for the baptism and about its celebration, songs and special clothing. Tell the stories and describe the day.

21

Letters from Grandparents

Grandchildren are the crown of the aged. Proverbs 17:6

Invite special letters from the grandparents, the whole extended family and the friends welcoming this child. Invite them to write about their own lives, their hopes and concerns, so that later the child can discover what often is never spoken.

Photos with grandparents/Early photos

Commemorative stamps

Lock of hair

Even the hairs of your head are all counted.

Luke 12:6

Our Faith, Our Church

This is our faith.
This is the faith of the church.
We are proud to profess it,
in Christ Jesus our Lord.
Amen. Liturgy of Baptism

Write here about how being Christian makes a difference in the family's life.

- The way we keep Sunday
- Morning prayers
- Meal prayers
- Prayers at bedtime • Family blessings
- Our church community
- What we want to hand on to this child

Your First Year

Lord our God,
the whole world tells
the greatness of your name.
Your glory reaches
beyond the stars.
Even the babble of infants
declares your strength. Psalm 8

Jot down the progress and details of the child's first 12 months. Tell the stories, simple or dramatic and positive or negative. These are the details and feelings that grow rich with time.
• Nursing and feeding • Sleeping patterns • Smiles, cooing, babbling, crying • Feelings and disposition

Birthdays

We are the only ones in creation who mark the anniversaries of our births. Birthdays allow us to "re-member," to put together the scattered pieces of our experience. Memory helps us make sense of who we are, and birthdays allow us to celebrate the miracle that we were born. The story of our birth fascinates us. It plants us firmly in time and space, and it reminds us of our unique identity before God and all creation. Birthdays even urge us to discover what our purpose here on earth might be.

Birthdays work best with reliable rituals for hearing our creation story, remembering the past year and looking to the future with hope. A good ritual helps us to pay attention to an occasion and give it importance. Rituals evolve as the birthdays come. They strengthen our identities. When they are deeply satisfying, we repeat them year after year. "In our family, we always. . . ." Consider these ideas:

• Anticipate the day! The night before, decorate! Hang streamers, set the table, put out the birthday mail, the birth certificate, a baby photo. On your prayer table, place the baptismal garment and candle.

• Before blowing out the candles on the cake, share something significant from the past year. Then, with a spoken blessing on the year to come, blow out the candles. Or invite each person to speak a wish or pronounce a blessing on the birthday person before the candles are blown out.

• Set out this book so that past years can be remembered, the birth story retold and new entries contributed.

• Perhaps the menu for that festive birthday meal includes something the parents remember eating on the day of this child's birth.

• For children, being weighed and measured can be a birthday ritual. Find a doorpost or make a growth chart to record and date the past year's growth.

First Birthday

**Keep straight the path of your feet,
and all your ways will be sure.** Proverbs 4:26

Mark the
child's height.

60"
59"
58"
57"
56"
55"
54"
53"
52"
51"
50"
49"
48"
47"
46"
45"
44"
43"
42"
41"
40"
39"
38"
37"
36"
35"
34"
33"
32"
31"
30"
29"
28"
27"
26"
25"
24"
23"
22"
21"
20"
19"
18"
17"
16"
15"
14"
13"
12"

Birthday photo

Your Second Year

For they ranged like horses,
and leaped like lambs,
praising you, O Lord, who delivered them. Wisdom 19:9

• Special friends, imaginary friends

• Pets • Fears

• Health • Toys, games • Songs

• Prayers learned and spontaneous

• Trips and adventures • Funny things • Serious things • Holidays: what we did

• Physical development and coordination

• First words and sentences

• Made-up words and their meanings • Caretakers • Favorite books and stories

• Changes in our family

• Major events in the world

Second Birthday

They shall run and not be weary,
they shall walk and not faint. Isaiah 40:31

60"
59"
58"
57"
56"
55"
54"
53"
52"
51"
50"
49"
48"
47"
46"
45"
44"
43"
42"
41"
40"
39"
38"
37"
36"
35"
34"
33"
32"
31"
30"
29"
28"
27"
26"
25"
24"
23"
22"
21"
20"
19"
18"
17"
16"
15"
14"
13"
12"

Birthday photo

Your Third Year

Keep these words that I am commanding you today in your heart. Recite them to your children and talk about them when you are at home and when you are away, when you lie down and when you rise.

Deuteronomy 6:6–7

• Special friends, imaginary friends
• Pets • Toys, Games • Fears
• Health
• Temperament
• Social development
• Songs and games • Prayers learned and spontaneous
• Trips and adventures • Funny things • Serious things • Wisdom shared • Holidays: what we did

• Physical achievements
• Potty events
• Caregivers
• Favorite books and stories
• Changes in our family
• Major events in the world

Third Birthday

The Lord bless you and keep you.
The Lord's face shine upon you
and be gracious to you.
The Lord give you peace. Numbers 6:24 – 25, 26

Mark the child's height.

60"
59"
58"
57"
56"
55"
54"
53"
52"
51"
50"
49"
48"
47"
46"
45"
44"
43"
42"
41"
40"
39"
38"
37"
36"
35"
34"
33"
32"
31"
30"
29"
28"
27"
26"
25"
24"
23"
22"
21"
20"
19"
18"
17"
16"
15"
14"
13"
12"

Birthday photo

Begin the birthday "two-envelope system" of granting privileges and responsibilities. One envelope contains an age-appropriate "new privilege," the other a "new responsibility." Growth brings longed-for privileges. And privileges are balanced with responsibilities. "Because you are three, you receive your very own cloth place mat and napkin at every meal." And: "Because you are three, you may help set the table for dinner." In the teen years, a set of keys to the family car is accompanied by a set of soft rags and car wax with a polishing schedule. A recipe book brings a schedule of visits to the community soup kitchen.

33

Your Fourth Year

**Bless the God of all,
who everywhere works great wonders,
who fosters our growth from birth,
and deals with us in mercy.** Sirach 50:22

• Special friends, imaginary friends

• Pets • Songs, games, stories

• Toys, books

• Joys • Fears

• Health • Prayers learned and spontaneous

• Sign of the cross

• Trips and adventures • Funny things • Serious things • Wisdom shared • Holidays: what we did

• Physical development

• Potty progress

• Caregivers

• Preschool

• Changes in our family • Numbers and alphabet

• Major events in the world

Fourth Birthday

God will cover you like a nesting bird.
God's wings will shelter you. Psalm 91

60"
59"
58"
57"
56"
55"
54"
53"
52"
51"
50"
49"
48"
47"
46"
45"
44"
43"
42"
41"
40"
39"
38"
37"
36"
35"
34"
33"
32"
31"
30"
29"
28"
27"
26"
25"
24"
23"
22"
21"
20"
19"
18"
17"
16"
15"
14"
13"
12"

Birthday photo

Your Fifth Year

- Special friends, imaginary friends
- Songs, games, books, stories
- Joys • Fears
- Prayers learned and spontaneous
- Favorite scripture stories
- Trips and adventures • Funny things • Serious things • Wisdom shared • Holidays: what we did

- Physical development
- Caregivers
- Preschool
- Numbers, alphabet and schoolwork
- Changes in our family

36

Fifth Birthday

**May the Lord Jesus, who loved children,
bless you and keep you.** *Catholic Household Blessings and Prayers*

Birthday photo and/or self-portrait

Parent and child can describe this day together. Take dictation. Encourage some illustrations. Write about the celebration: guests, gifts, cards, cake, joys, concerns, wishes made, thanks offered, blessings bestowed, special memories of the past year and hopes for the future. Tell about the new privilege and new responsibility. Collect and date examples of the child's drawings and dictated stories.

60"
59"
58"
57"
56"
55"
54"
53"
52"
51"
50"
49"
48"
47"
46"
45"
44"
43"
42"
41"
40"
39"
38"
37"
36"
35"
34"
33"
32"
31"
30"
29"
28"
27"
26"
25"
24"
23"
22"
21"
20"
19"
18"
17"
16"
15"
14"
13"
12"

Your Sixth Year

Jesus said, "Let the little children come to me, and do not stop them; for it is to such as these that the kingdom of heaven belongs."

Matthew 19:14

- Special friends
- Pets • Toys, books, stories
- Songs, games
- Joys • Fears
- Prayers learned and spontaneous
- Favorite scripture stories • Trips and adventures
- Funny things
- Serious things
- Wisdom shared
- Holidays: what we did • Physical development
- School and skills • Changes in our family
- Major events in the world

Sixth Birthday

Bless, O Christ, my face,
let my face bless everything.
Bless, O Christ, my eyes,
let my eyes bless all they see. *Celtic Prayers*

60"
59"
58"
57"
56"
55"
54"
53"
52"
51"
50"
49"
48"
47"
46"
45"
44"
43"
42"
41"
40"
39"
38"
37"
36"
35"
34"
33"
32"
31"
30"
29"
28"
27"
26"
25"
24"
23"
22"
21"
20"
19"
18"
17"
16"
15"
14"
13"
12"

Birthday photo and/or self-portrait

The Grade School Years

May God surround you with love and bring you many years.

Adapted from the *Book of Blessings*

Over these childhood years, make it a habit to write to and with the child using any method or style, occasion or inspiration. Birthdays, celebrations, special moments, blessings, privileges and responsibilities will always want a place in memory. Encourage the child's contributions through illustrations, written stories, school papers, family portraits and self-portraits.

Health and Hurts

Keep a loving eye on me.
Guard me under your wings. Psalm 17

Keep the immunization records here. Record nutrition and fitness programs, health check–ups, dentist visits, childhood diseases, accidents and illnesses. Include the child's own drawings and words about hurts, sickness and getting well. This also may be a place for the Tooth Fairy to keep the first lost tooth. Don't forget to celebrate an occasional "well day" in thanksgiving and joy for all these wonderful parts of us that work perfectly. Eat an apple today, and keep the doctor away.

- Ears • Eyes

- Nose and throat

- Stomach

- Teeth • Hurts

- Illnesses

- Healthy food

- Prayers for

good health

- Illnesses of

friends • Stories

and drawings

about sickness

and recovery

Immunization records

Feasts of Winter

O come, O come, Emmanuel. Advent chant

Feasts of Spring

We must not hide this story from our children but tell the mighty works and all the wonders of God. Psalm 78

Feasts of Summer

**The sky tells the glory of God,
tells the genius of God's work.
The sun springs from the edge of the earth,
runs a course across the sky.** Psalm 19

- What we did on Memorial Days
- Summer gardens and summer fruits
- Midsummer's Night (June 24): The bonfire of St. John the Baptist
- Fourth of July
- The Night of Shooting Stars (August 11)
- Assumption of Mary: herb and harvest feast (August 15)
- Summer vacations
- Back-to-school
- Labor Days

Feasts of Autumn

For all the saints who from their labors rest . . .

Hymn by William How

Prayers

**Lord, open my lips,
and my mouth
will proclaim your praise.**

Morning Prayer

Set up a quiet corner in the home with a chair and a prayer table where family members, no matter their age, can come to collect their thoughts and offer their prayers. Gather here for family prayer. Use incense, candles, flowers. Find an icon or a cross. Put pictures here of the people or situations you want to remember in your prayers.

Make a collection of prayers that grows up with this child. When children are very small, they can learn to fold their hands or raise them in praise. Later, they can complete rhyming prayers with you. Sing the prayers sometimes. Memorize a prayer. Grow into the psalms. Find a special meal prayer for Sundays. Encourage spontaneous prayer. A prayer life needs to evolve as we grow. Put the child's favorite prayers here.

Sacraments

**The Lord is my shepherd,
I need nothing more.
Goodness and love will tend me
every day of my life.** Psalm 23

What was begun at baptism is brought to fullness in the anointing of confirmation and full participation in the Sunday eucharist. The young child joins with the parish church to give thanks and praise to God around the altar, then to share in the bread and wine that have become for us the body and blood of Christ.

Write about the preparation for and celebration of these sacraments. Invite letters from the child's godparents, and save them on pages 18–19. Keep photos from the days of celebration.

Talk about the sacrament of reconciliation. And if the child becomes very ill or in need of surgery, enter here the experience of the sacrament of anointing.

Feelings and Growth of Character

You search me, Lord,
    and know me.
Wherever I sit or stand,
you read my inmost thoughts.
Before a word slips
    from my tongue,
Lord, you know what I will say.

Psalm 139

To be whole and healthy people, we need to know our feelings, name them and express them appropriately. This takes a vocabulary and practice! Here are pages for naming those strong emotions when they come and describing or drawing what they feel like. Tell the stories that surrounded times of frustration or joy, anger or happiness, sadness or longing, jealousy or generosity. Write about surprises, disagreements and hurt feelings, how these were expressed and the ways reconciliation and peace were restored.

Dreams

**No nighttime terror shall you fear,
no arrows shot by day,
no plague that prowls the dark.** Psalm 91

Some families and cultures make it a habit to share their dreams in the morning. Write them here and encourage the child to illustrate these dreams.

Keep watch, dear Lord, with those who work, or watch, or weep this night, and give your angels charge over those who sleep. Tend the sick, Lord Christ. Give rest to the weary, bless the dying, soothe the suffering, pity the afflicted, shield the joyous; and all for your love's sake. Amen.

A night prayer by St. Augustine

People We Pray For

Ask, and it will be given you. Matthew 7:7

Especially at the end of the day, we pray to the Lord for our families and friends and for all in need. Put names, drawings and photos on this page.

- Family members, relatives

- Friends • Teachers

- Neighbors • Government

leaders • Church leaders • The

sick • The dying • Those who

mourn • The poor • Prisoners

We Remember Those Who Have Died

Eternal rest grant unto them, O Lord,
and let perpetual light shine upon them.
May their souls
and the souls of all the faithful departed,
through the mercy of God,
rest in peace. Amen. Order of Christian Funerals

Record the names and dates of family members, friends and others who have died. Tell their stories.

Special Happenings

I see your handiwork
in the heavens:
the moon and the stars
you set in place.

What is humankind
that you remember them,
the human race
that you care for them? Psalm 8

Here are pages
for writing about
new sisters and
brothers and
cousins. About
moves from an
old home to a
new home. About
special experi-
ences with nature:
seeds, flowers,
bugs, caterpillars,
butterflies,
birds, water, fish,
forest, shore,
mountains, rain,
snow, sky, clouds,
sun, moon, stars

Growing Up

God shields you,
a protector by your side.
The sun shall not harm you by day
nor the moon at night.
God shelters you from evil,
securing your life.
God watches over you near and far,
now and always. Psalm 121

As this child grows into a unique personality and temperament and develops talents, observe and make notes. Describe what is wondrously happening. Tell what gives this child particular joy or anxious concern. • Graciousness and courtesy • Responsibility • Mannerisms • Passions • Dislikes • Conscience development • Talents • Foibles • Accomplishments • Awards • Struggles • Sensitivities • Social attitudes

59

Putting This Book Away

**Let future generations learn
and let them grow up
to teach their young
to trust in God,
remembering great deeds,
cherishing the law.** Psalm 78

When this book has served its purpose, decide on a
day when it will be closed with ceremony and intention.
Write a final letter, date it, seal it in an envelope,
and attach it to this page. Then put the book away for
an important occasion or rite of passage in this
child's future.

Photos from the day this book was put away

After the Passage of Time:
Receiving This Book as a Young Adult

Date _____

Place _____

Occasion _____

Photos

Love is patient; love is kind;
love is not envious or boastful
or arrogant or rude.
It bears all things,
believes all things,
hopes all things,
endures all things.
Love never ends. 1 Corinthians 13:4, 7 – 8